CATCH A RAINBOW

GENERAL EDITOR

JACK BOOTH

DAVID BOOTH

WILLA PAULI & JO PHENIX

IMPRESSIONS

HOLT, RINEHART AND WINSTON OF CANADA, LIMITED

Sponsoring Editor: Sheba Meland
Senior Editor: Wendy Cochran
Production Editor: Jocelyn Van Huyse
Art Director: Wycliffe Smith
Design Assistant: Julia Naimska
Cover Illustrator: Heather Cooper

ISBN 0-03-921403-6

Canadian Cataloguing in Publication Data

Main entry under title:
Catch a Rainbow

(Impressions)
For use in schools.
ISBN 0-03-921403-6

1. Readers (Primary).   2. Readers – 1950 –
I. Booth, Jack   II. Series.

PE1119.M39   428.6   C83-098246-9

Illustrations

Frank Hammond: pp. 4-10, 60-63; *Mary Young*: pp. 11-16; *Vera B. Williams*: pp. 17-19; *David Partington*: pp. 20-29; *Bill Harrison*: pp. 30-31; *John Burningham*: pp. 32-40; *Elizabeth Bridgman*: pp. 41-46; *Magda Markowski*: pp. 47-57; *Barbara Klunder*: pp. 58-59; *Joe Weissmann*: pp. 64-66; *Eugenie Fernandés*: pp. 67-80.

The authors and publishers gratefully acknowledge the consultants listed below for their contribution to the development of this program:

Isobel Bryan   *Primary Consultant   Ottawa Board of Education*
Ethel Buchanan   *Language Arts Consultant   Winnipeg, Manitoba*
Heather Hayes   *Elementary Curriculum Consultant   City of Halifax Board of Education*
Gary Heck   *Curriculum Co-ordinator, Humanities   Lethbridge School District No. 51*
Ina Mary Rutherford   *Supervisor of Reading and Primary Instruction   Bruce County Board of Education*
Janice M. Sarkissian   *Supervisor of Instruction (Primary and Pre-School)   Greater Victoria School District*
Lynn Taylor   *Language Arts Consultant   Saskatoon Catholic School Board*

Acknowledgements

Printed in Canada   8 9   91 90 89 88

Table of Contents

What Will I Wear?
by
David Booth

Here is my hat.
It is orange.

Here is my T-shirt.
It is red.

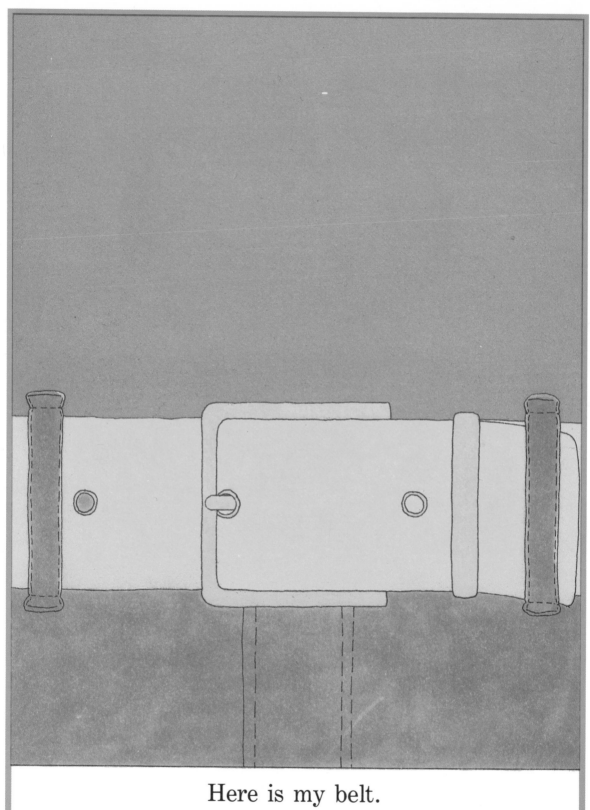

Here is my belt.
It is yellow.

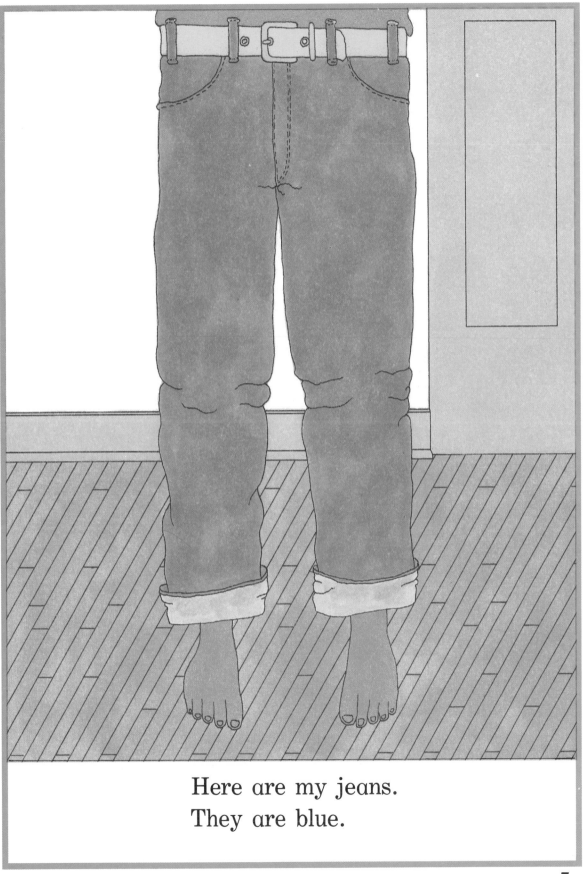

Here are my jeans.
They are blue.

Here are my socks.
They are green.

Here are my shoes.
They are purple.

Here is a rainbow.
(Sometimes it hides in my closet.)

In the Park

by
Meguido Zola

PLEASE WALK ON THE GRASS

My dog and I like the park.

We feed the ducks.

duck pond

We buy ice cream.

ice cream 60¢

DEPOSIT LITTER HERE

12

We skip.

We play catch.

We read.

We swim.

We have a picnic.

We fly kites.

We play with our friends.

We ride our bikes.

BICYCLE
PATH

16

Hooray for Me!

by
Remy Charlip, Lilian Moore, and
Vera B. Williams

WHATEVER I WAS
WHATEVER I'LL BE
HOORAY FOR YOU!
HOORAY FOR ME!

WHATEVER YOU DO
WHATEVER YOU'LL BE
HOORAY FOR YOU!
HOORAY FOR ME!

HOORAY FOR US!
WHATEVER WE BE
HOORAY FOR YOU!
HOORAY FOR ME!

HOORAY FOR ME! HOORAY FOR YOU! AND ME! AND YOU! HOORAY FOR ME! AND YOU! HOORAY FOR YOU! AND ME! HOORAY FOR ME. HOORAY FOR YOU, ME! HOORAY FOR YOU! HOORAY FOR YOU! HOORAY FOR TWO! HOORAY FOR ME! HOORAY FOR THREE! HOORAY FOR YOU!

HOORAY FOR WHO?

18

Do Baby Bears Sit in Chairs?
by
Ethel and Leonard Kessler

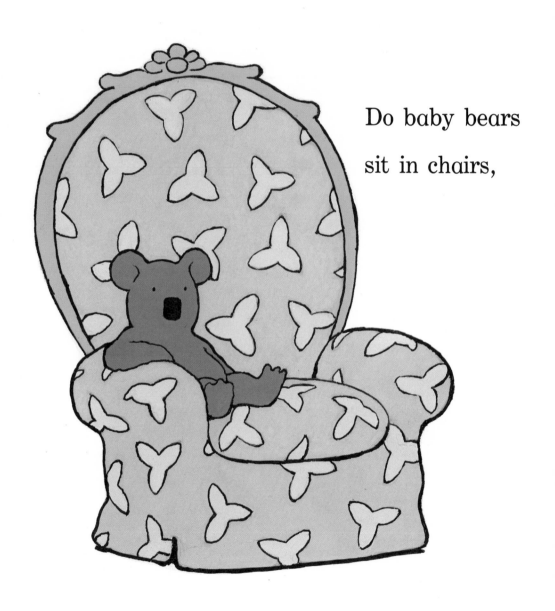

Do baby bears

sit in chairs,

comb their hair,

wear underwear?

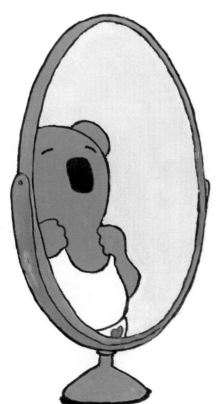

NO!

But
    they
        roll
            down
                the hill,
                    just as I do.

Can kangaroos read the news,

play peek-a-boo,

sing "Skip to My Loo"?

Oh, no, no, no!
But they can
hop, hop,
hop,

just as I do.

I am hopping,

I am jumping,

I am crawling,

I am rolling,

falling.

BOOM!

Canadian Alphabet

by
Meguido Zola

AB CD EF G
Say the alphabet with me,
HI JK LM N
Write it down with ink and pen,
OP QR S and T
Read it back out loud to me,
UV W XYZ
Now it's always in your head.

B.HARRISON

The School
by
John Burningham

When I go to school

I learn to read,

and to write,

sing songs,

eat my lunch,

paint pictures,

play games,

make friends,

and then go home.

New Dog Next Door
by
Elizabeth Bridgman

There's a new dog next door
and he is big.

He is very big!

I think he likes me.

He likes my father, too,
and my baby sister.

He brings my mother presents
and sits by our door.

He likes to ride in our car
and sleep in our garage.

He takes out our garbage
and guards our house.

And he's not even our dog!
We have never had a dog.

But I think we have one now.

Ten Green Bottles
Traditional

Ten green bottles are hanging on the wall.

Nine green bottles are hanging on the wall.

Eight green bottles are hanging on the wall.

Seven green bottles are hanging on the wall.

Six green bottles are hanging on the wall.

Five green bottles are hanging on the wall.

Four green bottles are hanging on the wall.

Three green bottles are hanging on the wall.

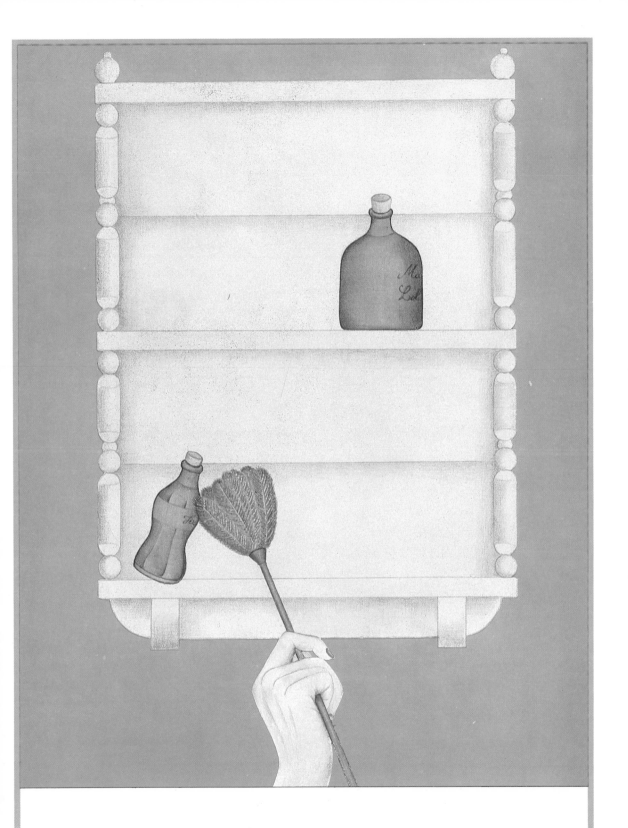

Two green bottles are hanging on the wall.

55

One green bottle is hanging on the wall.

If that green bottle should accidentally fall,
there'd be no green bottles hanging on the wall.

Wiggles and Squiggles
by
Dr. Fitzhugh Dodson

Watch me.

Watch me squirm.

I'm pretending I'm a worm.

I wiggle my fingers.

I wiggle my toes.

I jiggle my ears.

I waggle my nose.

Watch me.

Watch me squirm.

I'm pretending I'm a worm.

My Teeth Bite
by
Jack Booth

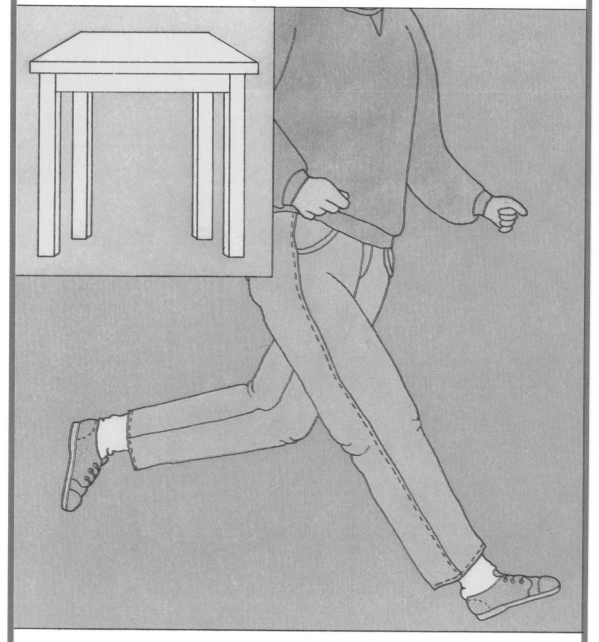

A table has legs. I have legs. But my legs run!

A chair has arms. I have arms. But my arms hug!

A clock has hands. I have hands. But my hands hold!

A comb has teeth. I have teeth. But my teeth bite!

Little Black Bug

by
Margaret Wise Brown

Little black bug,
Little black bug,
Where have you been?

I've been under the rug,
Said little black bug.
Bug-ug-ug-ug.

Little green fly,
Little green fly,
Where have you been?

I've been way up high,
Said little green fly.
Bzzzzzzzzzzzzzz.

Little old mouse,
Little old mouse,
Where have you been?

I've been all through the house,
Said little old mouse.
Squeak-eak-eak-eak-eak.

Goodnight Owl
by
Pat Hutchins

Owl tried to sleep.

The squirrel cracked nuts,
crunch crunch,
and Owl tried to sleep.

The crows croaked,
caw caw,
and Owl tried to sleep.

The jays screamed,
ark ark,
and Owl tried to sleep.

The cuckoo called,
cuckoo cuckoo,
and Owl tried to sleep.

The woodpecker pecked,
rat-a-tat, *rat-a-tat*,
and Owl tried to sleep.

The starlings chittered,
twit-twit, *twit-twit*,
and Owl tried to sleep.

The doves cooed,
croo croo,
and Owl tried to sleep.

The bees buzzed,
buzz buzz.
The squirrel cracked nuts,
crunch crunch.
The crows croaked,
caw caw.
The woodpecker pecked,
rat-a-tat, rat-a-tat.
The starlings chittered,
twit-twit, twit-twit.

The robin peeped,
pip pip,
and Owl tried to sleep.

The sparrows chirped,
cheep cheep,
and Owl tried to sleep.

The jays screamed,
ark ark.
The cuckoo called,
cuckoo cuckoo.
The robin peeped,
pip pip.
The sparrows chirped,
cheep cheep.
The doves cooed,
croo croo,
and Owl couldn't sleep.

Then darkness fell
and the moon came up.
And there wasn't a sound.

Owl screeched,
screech screech,
and woke everyone up.